Contents

How We See Things

Changing Circuits

Answers to the questions are on the back of the Pull-out Poster in the centre of the book.

This book covers unit 6F from the year six scheme of work

Published by CGP

Contributors:
Angela Billington
Chris Dennett
Lindsay Jordan
Tim Major
Katherine Stewart
Claire Thompson
Tim Wakeling
Suzanne Worthington

ISBN: 978 1 84146 272 1

Groovy website: www.cgpbooks.co.uk

Jolly bits of clipart from CorelDRAW®

Printed by Elanders Ltd, Newcastle upon Tyne.

Based on the classic CGP style created by Richard Parsons.

Background — How We See Things

Hmm... seeing things. Dead easy, you do it all day without even thinking about it. But tough toffee, pal, you've gotta know a bit more than that — like what <u>shadows</u> and <u>reflections</u> are, about shiny and dull surfaces, and how you can make light <u>change direction</u>. Phew.

Q1   Draw Peter's shadow on the picture below. (I don't know why he's smashing nuts on the road, he just is, OK.)

The shadow didn't scare Billy, but the thing causing the shadow did.

Q2   Label the light source on the picture above by writing "light source" and putting an arrow pointing to it. (Hint: the light source is where the light is coming from.)

Q3   Fill in the blanks to finish off the paragraph below, using words from the shadow.

Light .... from the ....

to the ......*ground*........ . If anything gets in its way

some of the light will be .... The light

that's blocked .... be able to reach the ground.

On the ground the light can't get to, there is a ....

area called a ....

To get out of the Sun, people sit in the ....

— which is the same as saying they sit in the shadows.

This ketchup's too heavy — I need a light source...

This page is just a taste of things to come — you'll do a lot more about <u>shadows</u> and <u>light sources</u>. I can't promise you any more pictures of people smashing nuts with a pan though. Sorry. ☺

Light Travels

It might seem a bit weird to think of light as an <u>actual thing</u>, but it is.
And when it shines on a house, it's <u>travelling</u> from the torch or whatever to the house.

Dave is keeping his neighbours awake by shining a searchlight onto their windows. Then a hot-air balloon flies between Dave and the wall, completely blocking all of the light.

Q1   Tick the correct explanation of why there's no light on the window in the second picture.

In the first picture, the light travels from the searchlight to the window. In the second picture, the light is attracted to the balloon, and sucked up by it. ☐

The balloon is <u>opaque</u> — that means light can't get through it.

☐ In the first picture, the light travels from the searchlight to the window. In the second picture it travels to the balloon, but gets blocked by it, so it can't get any further. Since it doesn't reach the window, you don't see the light on the window.

Q2   Dave does an experiment to find out what's happening. He shines a torch at a wall, and can see the light on the wall. Then he moves some card between the torch and the wall. He can still see some light on the wall, but it's a different shape.

a)   Write out these sentences in the right order to make an explanation of what happens.

Part of the light can travel to the wall, but part gets blocked by the card.

Then he moves the card part way in front of the torch.

When Dave turns on the torch, the light shines from it to the wall.

....

....

....

b)   What will happen if Dave moves the card all the way in front of the light?

....

....

Light torches — much better than heavy torches...

The point of all this is that light <u>travels</u> from the torch, lamp or whatever. It travels to the wall or any other opaque thing, and that's where you can <u>see it</u>. <u>Don't</u> go thinking light just <u>flows around</u>.

Light Travels into Your Eyes

Everybody knows that light is really important to be able to <u>see</u>, but you've probably never thought about how it all <u>works</u>. Light <u>travels into</u> your eyes to let you see. Think about it...

Q1 Here are 8 things in light or in darkness. Some of them you would be able to see and some of them you wouldn't — write each one in the correct place in the table. Underneath each one write 'YES' if the object gives out light and 'NO' if it doesn't.

A torch switched on in the dark.   A torch switched off in the dark.   Glow worms in the dark.   A banana in the dark.

A giraffe in the dark.   A giraffe in the light.   Me in the dark.   A banana in the light.

You would be able to see it.				
Gives out light?				

You would <u>not</u> be able to see it.				
Gives out light?				

Light has to travel into your eyes for you to be able to see. That means that you can only see things in a dark room if they give out light themselves, unless they are lit up by another light source.

Q2 In question 1 there are two examples with a torch. Could you see the torch in both? Why do you think this is?   (Clue: think about whether they give out light or not.)

....

....

....

Q3 Why wouldn't you be able to see some of the objects in question 1? (Circle) the right sentence.

There is no light.   There is too much light.   You have shut your eyes.   They have turned invisible.

Q4 There were other objects apart from the torch and the glow worms that you could see. Why could you see them?

No really, I'm <u>not</u> your dog. I'm a giraffe!

Miriam couldn't see very well in her new hat.

....

"Doctor, doctor, everything's dark" — "Open your eyes"

Light doesn't come from your eyes — you see things when light travels <u>into</u> your eyes. If there <u>wasn't</u> any light from things like torches or light bulbs or the Sun, you <u>wouldn't</u> see anything.

Light Can Be Reflected

Mirrors and other shiny surfaces <u>reflect light</u>. This means that light hits the surface and bounces off. The 'bounced off' light is the reflection that you see. If you position the mirror properly, you can see reflections from all kinds of places — even around <u>corners</u>.

Q1   What can these three dentists see with their mirrors? Choose the right answers from the choices below and write them underneath the pictures.

Behind his shoulder   **Through the wall**   **Into the patient's mind**   **Between his feet**

Behind the patient's teeth   **Around the corner of the wall**

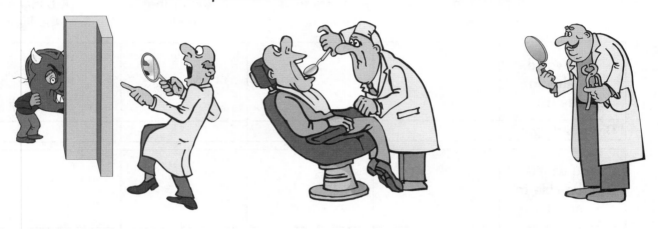

....

Q2   Circle the right words to finish off this paragraph about reflections.

When light hits a mirror, the light   IS REFLECTED / GOES THROUGH IT .   You can see reflections

in mirrors, on water, or on   HAIRY / SHINY   surfaces like   WINDOWS / DOGS .   You can use a

mirror to   SEE / HEAR   what you   SOUND / LOOK   like, because the light travels from your face

to the mirror, where it's   REFLECTED / LOST   and comes back to your eyes.

Q3   For each of the pictures below, put a tick in the box if Jill's mirror is helping her to find her pet monster. Put a cross in the box if the mirror isn't helping her to see the monster.

Not feeling too bright? — Sit down and reflect on it...

All you need to remember is that light from an object (like Jill's monster) can be <u>reflected</u> by a mirror. You see the <u>image</u> of the object when the reflected light enters your eyes.

Light Can Be Reflected

Some light sources, like electric torches, have a <u>narrow beam</u> of light. Others, like bonfires, light up everything around them in <u>all directions</u>. That's dead <u>tricky</u> to show in a drawing — unless you know about this useful tip...

A good way to show what happens to light from a light source is to draw straight lines for rays of light, and to put arrows on them to show what direction they go in.

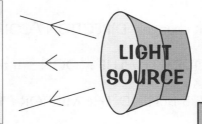

The dentist would need a good light source to find his mirror.

Q1 For each of the light sources below, choose which arrows show the direction of the light from the source. Write the number of the correct arrows in the box.

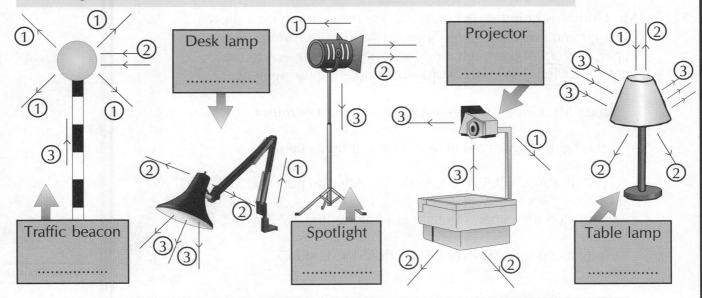

Traffic beacon ....

Desk lamp ....

Spotlight ....

Projector ....

Table lamp ....

Q2 Using the info at the top of the page, draw the directions of the light in each of these pictures. Remember that the light may be travelling in lots of directions at once.

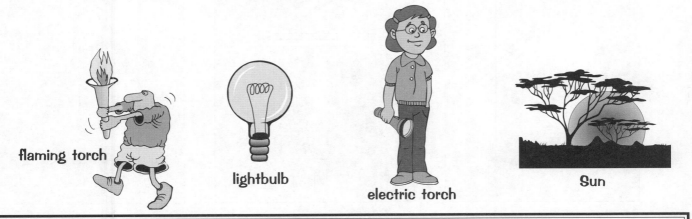

flaming torch

lightbulb

electric torch

Sun

It's my headlamps — they're making me light-headed...

Flippin' marvellous. A simple little line with an arrow on it to show what <u>direction</u> a beam or ray of light is travelling in. This really is the <u>best thing</u> since pickled cabbage...

What Happens when Light is Reflected

When light hits a surface, it can be __reflected__. That's what happens
with mirrors and shop windows where you can see your reflection.

Q1   Cross out the wrong words in these sentences.

When light hits a mirror, it changes DIRECTION / COLOUR . That's why, if you look straight in a

mirror, you can see YOURSELF / THE MOON . If the light went straight through the mirror,

you'd see WHATEVER IS BEHIND THE MIRROR / YOURSELF . When you draw a light ray

hitting the mirror, you should draw the ray changing direction BEFORE / WHEN it hits the mirror.

Q2   Mr. Grimes is doing an experiment. He puts a torch on a piece
of paper and switches it on. Then he stands a mirror up on the
paper, in front of the torch, and looks at what happens to the
light ray. (Circle) the right words to complete these sentences.

When Mr. Grimes shines the torch without the mirror,

the light ray goes along line A / B . It lights up the

TENNIS BALL / PLASTIC CARROT . After he puts the

mirror on the paper, the light goes along line A / B .

It lights up the TENNIS BALL / PLASTIC CARROT .

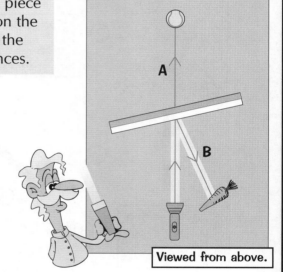

Viewed from above.

Q3   In these pictures, finish the drawing of the light beam, and draw the light
rays (as lines with arrows on them) going to the mirror and reflecting off it.

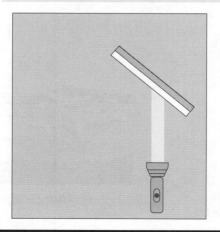 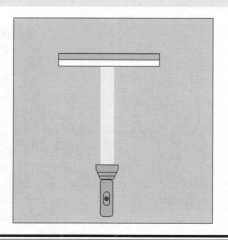 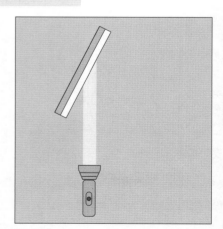

And yet another one......gag reflecting Another

When a light ray hits a mirror, it will be __reflected__ (i.e. bounce off it). When the ray __hits__ the mirror
at different __angles__, it __bounces off__ at different angles too. Try it out with a mirror, torch and paper.

What Happens when Light is Reflected

Careful with this page — it's about what <u>direction</u> the light bounces off the mirror. It depends on what direction the light hits the mirror to start with.

Q1   In each of these pictures, look at the light ray going from the torch and circle the correct ray (1, 2 or 3) that is reflected from the mirror.

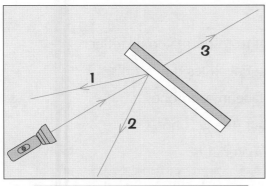

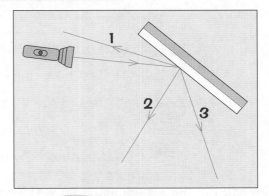

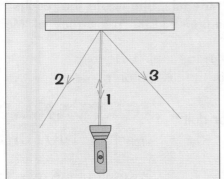

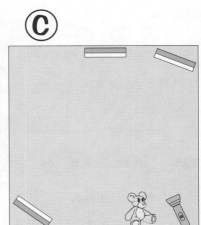

Barry was sure there was something wrong with his hairdresser's mirror.

Q2   Kate wants to build a set of mirrors that will send the light from her torch <u>all the way round</u> her nasty pet bear. She's trying out three different sets. In each of these pictures, draw the rays with arrows on them to show where the light would go. When it hits an object or a wall, draw a blob at the end of the arrow.

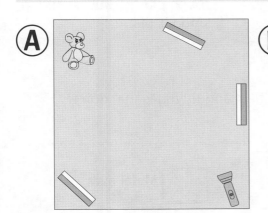

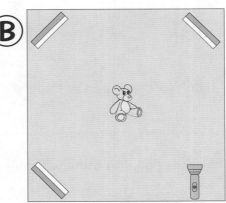

Q3   Which set of mirrors will work?   ....

Light rays are best — so no heavy ones please...

As long as you know that light <u>bounces off</u> mirrors, and that means light <u>changes direction</u> when it hits a mirror, then you understand mirrors. If you can, <u>have a go</u> at doing the kind of thing in Q2.

Reflecting — Shiny vs Dull

This is all about whether or not materials <u>reflect</u>.

Wendy's planning an experiment to find out which materials reflect light. She thought of lots of different ways of doing the experiment and wrote them down on her 'iN-Sink' pad.

Q1 Put a (circle) around the best way of doing the experiment.

How I could do an experiment to test if materials reflect:

1) Test how quickly each material slides down hills.
2) Test to see if I can see my face in each one.
3) Test to see how quickly each one gets hot.
4) Measure how bendy each material is.

Wendy did the experiment with 6 different types of material. She wrote the results down in her 'MotorBed' pad. (She'd gone off iN-Sink's music — she preferred the 'pillow-rock' of 'MotorBed'.)

Q2 Write out Wendy's results in the first two columns in the table below.
Then write whether each material is shiny or dull in the last column.

Name of material	Does it reflect?	Is it shiny or dull?

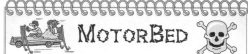

MotorBed

<u>Result of the reflection test:</u>
I couldn't see my face in the wood, but I could in the silver. I could see my face in the glass but not in the wool. I couldn't see my face in the rough plastic, but I could in the smooth plastic.

Q3 What is the difference between the materials that do reflect and the ones that don't?

....

Q4 Put a tick next to the materials that you think will reflect.

Metal spoon

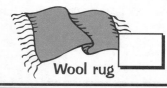

Wool rug

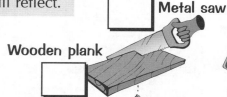

Metal saw

Wooden plank

Gold bar

It keeps hiding behind my leg — it's a SHY KNEE...

There's a simple rule to work out whether or not something reflects — if it's <u>shiny</u> it <u>reflects</u>, if it's <u>dull</u> it <u>doesn't</u>. Told you it was simple — now, repeat after me, "shiny reflects, dull doesn't".

Shadows

You can change the <u>size</u> of an object's shadow — on this page you get to work out <u>how</u>.

Q1 I want to find out what changes the size of a shadow. I'm going to do an experiment. Here's a picture of the equipment I'll use.

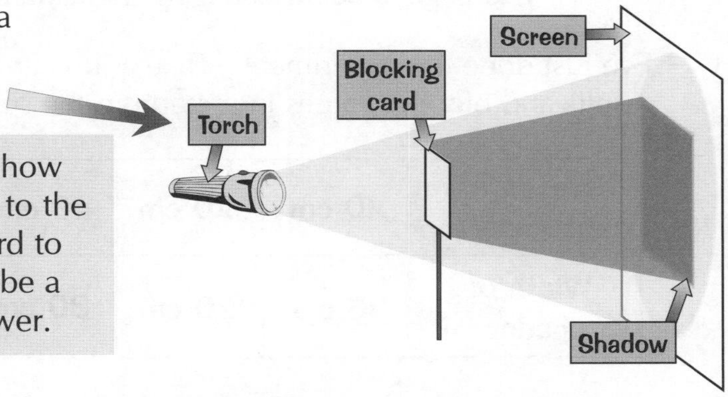

The two things I want to find out about are how changing the distance from the light source to the card and changing the distance from the card to the screen affect the shadow. What would be a good way to find out? (Circle) the right answer.

[Diagram labels: Torch, Blocking card, Screen, Shadow]

Change both distances at once every time you take a measurement.

Change only one distance at a time until you know how one affects the shadow. Then keep that one the same and change the other.

Keep both distances the same all the way through the experiment.

Q2 Why is your answer to Q1 the best way to do the experiment? Tick (✔) the right answer.

If you change both distances at once, you'll know how they affect each other. ☐

If you change both distances at once, you can do the experiment quicker. ☐

If you changed both things at once, you won't know which one had made the difference. ☐

Q3 a) Hannah's going to do the experiment. She's planning to hold the torch at different angles each time. Could this change the results?

....

b) Would you be able to tell whether the results were changed by the angle she held the torch or by the distance she tested?

....

c) So is her plan a good idea or a bad idea?

....

Hannah wondered if she could make her shadow bigger by feeding it cake.

<u>*I just want to distance myself from this page...*</u>

Every time you do an experiment, you've got to make sure it's a <u>fair test</u>. That means that you only change <u>one thing</u> at a time — otherwise your results won't tell you anything useful at all.

Shadows

Now that you've worked out how to keep the test **fair**, the experiment can begin.
This page is about changing the distance from the **blocking card** to the **screen**.

Q1   I've just done the experiment. Take a look at my table of
results and plot the values in a graph in the space below.

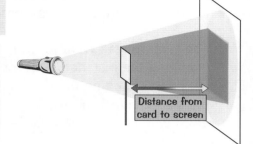

Distance from card to screen	10 cm	20 cm	40 cm	60 cm
Width of shadow	15 cm	20 cm	30 cm	40 cm

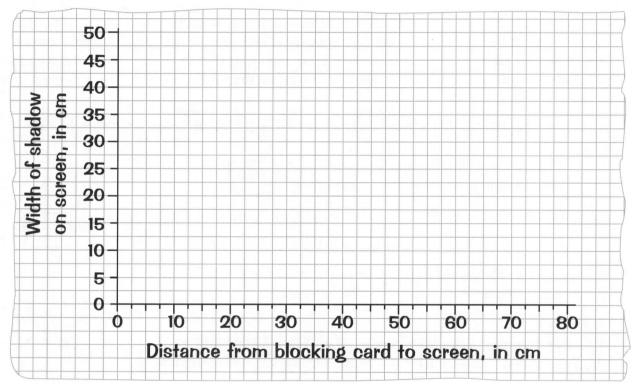

Q2   Does the distance from the card to the screen
make any difference to the size of the shadow? ....

Q3   Use the graph to predict the width of the
shadow if the screen was 30 cm from the card. ....

Q4   This time, use the graph to predict
the width of the shadow if the
screen was 80 cm from the card. ....

[Hint: use a ruler to continue the line on the graph up to 80 cm, then read off the width.]

Liam was in a hurry and
didn't have time to do
experiments with his torch.

Shadow magician — Light Sorcerer?...

Now you'll know **exactly** how the distance between the card and the screen affects the shadow,
without me giving you any clues. And the next page has **even more** about shadows — lucky you...

Coming soon — page 12...

Shadows

I know you loved that last page, so here's <u>another</u> one that's a lot like it —
this time it's all about changing the distance from the <u>light source</u> to the <u>blocking card</u>.

Q1 Use this table of results to plot the values in a whole new graph.

Distance from torch to card	10 cm	20 cm	30 cm	50 cm
Width of shadow	35 cm	25 cm	20 cm	13 cm

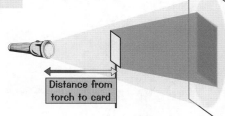

Distance from torch to card

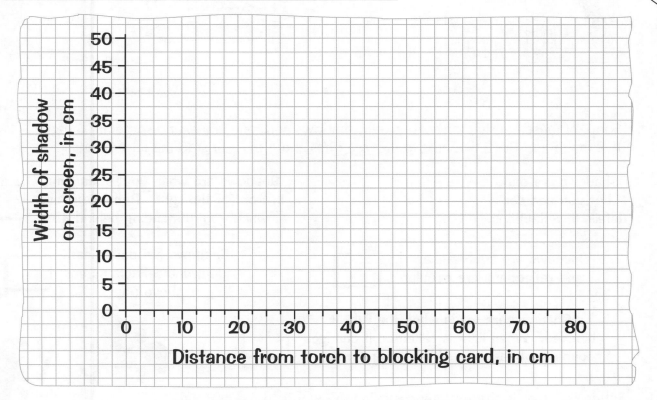

Q2 Does the distance from the light source to the card make any difference to the size of the shadow?

....

Bonzo knew all about making his shadow look bigger.

Q3 Use the graph to predict the width of the shadow if the card was 40 cm from the torch.

....

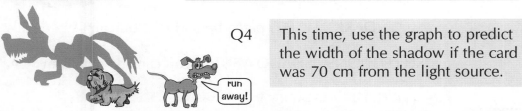

run away!

Q4 This time, use the graph to predict the width of the shadow if the card was 70 cm from the light source.

....

I predict that you're sick of predictions by now...

You should be good at all this stuff by now. Making predictions is a lot easier if you're working from a <u>graph</u> instead of just taking loads more <u>readings</u> — you can save yourself <u>a lot</u> of time.

...it's almost here...

Shadows and Reflections

Now you know about <u>shadows</u> and <u>reflections</u>, you need to be able to tell them <u>apart</u>.

Q1 Take a look at these pictures, then label each one with SHADOW or REFLECTION.

....

....

....

....

....

....

Q2 Some of these are differences between shadows and reflections, and some are things I've made up. Put a tick next to the true ones and a cross next to the false ones.

Shadows are dark, but you can see details in reflections. ☐

Shadows are when you're standing in front of the light. Reflections are when you're standing behind it. ☐

Shadows are square-shaped, and reflections are circular. ☐

Shadows are underneath you, and reflections are above you. ☐

Shadows are made when the light is blocked. When light is reflected it changes direction because it hits a shiny surface. ☐

Why are we shadows?

I guess it saved time for the artist.

Q3 Fill in the gaps in these sentences using the words in the brackets.

Reflections happen when light hits a .... (SHINY / DULL) surface

like a mirror, and changes .... (COLOUR / DIRECTION). Shadows

are when something is .... (LOOKING AT / BLOCKING) the light, so

there is a .... (DARK / LIGHT) patch behind it. You can't see details

in .... (REFLECTIONS / SHADOWS), but you can see details in

.... (REFLECTIONS / SHADOWS).

Sit back and reflect on the work you've done...

Shadows and reflections happen for <u>different</u> reasons — make sure you're clued up on the difference. If you think reflections and shadows are the same thing, then you're <u>way off track</u>. They aren't.

KS2 Science Answers — How We See Things & Changing Circuits

Page 13 Revision Questions

Q1: a) "A lit candle", "a searchlight (switched on)" & "a fire" should be circled.

b) "I would see them because light would travel from the objects to my eyes" should be circled.

Q2: When light hits a **SHINY** surface, it is reflected. That's how you see your **REFLECTION** when you look in a mirror. The light changes **DIRECTION** when it's reflected, depending on what direction the light has travelled from.

Q3: a) Because the card stops some of the light from hitting the screen.

b) The shadow gets smaller.

c) The shadow gets bigger.

d) There is no light on the screen and no shadow.

Q4:
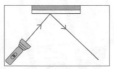

Page 14 You Can Change the Brightness of a Bulb

Q1: You can make this bulb brighter by adding another **BATTERY** to the circuit. Or, you could use a battery with a **HIGHER VOLTAGE**. But if you added another **BULB** to the circuit, there would be less **POWER** for each bulb, so both bulbs would be **DIMMER** than the original one.

Q2: a) The second box should be ticked, because higher voltage gives more power.

b) The second box should be ticked, because higher voltage gives more power.

c) The first box should be ticked because there is only one bulb in the circuit.

d) The top box should be ticked because higher voltage gives more power.

Page 15 You Can Change the Speed of a Motor

Q1: a) The first motor will run faster. b) The first motor will run faster.

c) The second motor will run faster. d) The second motor will run faster.

Q2: Something along these lines:

The battery gives too much power — so the motor will burn out.

Page 16 Too Much Power Will Burn Things Out

Q1: When you connect a **MORE POWERFUL** battery in a circuit with a bulb, it'll glow **BRIGHTER**. But if the battery's voltage is **TOO HIGH**, the bulb gets really hot and will **BURN OUT**. And you **CAN'T** get it to work again after that.

Q2: You can speed up a motor by using a battery with a **HIGHER VOLTAGE**. But if the **BATTERY** has too high a voltage, the motor burns out.

Q3: "The bulb will burn out" should be ticked.

Q4: The motor will burn out.

Q5: Burns out Glows Burns out Doesn't glow

Page 17 Circuit Diagrams and Symbols

Q1: Road signs **DON'T** have lots of writing on them. For example, a 'no **LEFT TURN** sign like this doesn't have any writing on it — just a crossed out picture of a left arrow. That's useful because it's **QUICK** and easy to **UNDERSTAND**.

Q2: a) "The same part looks different in each drawing" and "she might not be able to tell the difference between motors and batteries in the drawings" should be ticked.

b) "Have a set of symbols so that everyone draws the parts of circuits in the same way" should be circled.

Page 18 Circuit Diagrams and Symbols

Q1: Right Wrong Wrong Right

Q2:
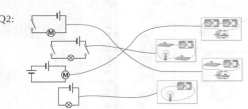

Page 19 Circuit Diagrams and Symbols

Q1:
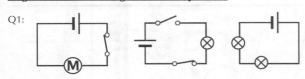

Q2:

Page 20 Wire Thickness — Fair Tests

Q1: "Test several thicknesses of wires..." should be circled.

Q2: Ed should make sure his experiment is a **FAIR TEST**. That means he should only change **ONE THING** at a time. If he changed the thickness of the wire and changed its length and got a different result from before, he **WOULDN'T** know whether it was because of the change in the thickness or the change in length.

Q3: "The length of the wire", "the material the wire is made from", "the strength of the battery" and "the thickness of the wires" should all be ticked.

Page 21 Wire Thickness — Results

Q1:
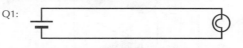

Q2:

Thickness of wire	Brightness of bulb
Very thick	Brightest
Thick	Next brightest
Thin	Dimmest

Page 22 Wire Thickness — Conclusions

Q1: Yes.

Q2: We wanted to test to see if the **THICKNESS** of a wire affects the brightness of a bulb in a circuit. We tested **THREE** different thicknesses of wire in **THREE** separate circuits. The bulb was brightest when we used the **VERY THICK** wire. The bulb was dimmest when we used the **THIN** wire.

Q3: The thicker the wire, the brighter the bulb.

The thinner the wire, the dimmer the bulb.

Q4: Ed should use the thickest wire.

Q5: "Replace the wires with thinner ones" should be ticked.

Page 23 Testing Different Wires

Q1: "Hair", "wood", "wool", "cotton", "plastic" and "paper" should be crossed out.

Q2:

Type of wire	Brightness of bulb
Lead	4
Iron	7
Copper	8
Gold	10

Q3: Ed should use the gold wire.

Q4: Test several lengths of wire and see how bright the bulb is in each circuit.

Page 24 Using Your Knowledge of Circuits

Q1: "They are using batteries and not mains electricity, so the voltage is low enough not be dangerous" should be ticked.

Q2: It's **OK** to use bare wires with batteries, because the voltage is so **LOW** that it isn't dangerous. Bare wires connected to the **MAINS** are very **DANGEROUS**. You should **NEVER** have bare wires on a mains electricity circuit.

Q3: Rubber and plastic should be ringed.

Q4: They do not conduct electricity and they won't melt.

Page 25 Revision Questions

Q1: a) An extra battery.

b) An extra lamp — because the power would be shared over two bulbs.

Q2: They would both turn at the same speed because both of the circuits have the same voltage from the batteries.

Q3: The first diagram should be ticked and the second one should be crossed.

Q4: Q5:
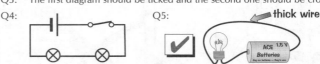

Q6: The gold wire — because the plastic wire would not work at all, and the copper wire would not make the bulb shine as brightly as the gold wire would.

Reflections

Reflections

Shadows &

The Shadows

New Album out now

Reflections

EDISON ALLEY

Arrows show the

Ray's Lighting

Light beams

Shadow made by chef's body blocking the light

CGP KS2 Science for Cats

From the CGP KS2 Science Book — How We See Things and Changing Circuits

KS2 Science Answers — How We See Things & Changing Circuits

Page 1 Background — How we See Things

Q1 & Q2:

Sun — Light source

Q3: Light **TRAVELS** from the **LIGHT SOURCE** to the ground. If anything gets in its way some of the light will be **BLOCKED**. The light that's blocked **WON'T** be able to reach the ground. On the ground which is blocked from the light source, there is a **DARK** area called a **SHADOW**. To get out of the Sun, people sit in the **SHADE** — which is the same as saying they sit in the shadows.

Page 2 Light Travels

Q1: The bottom box should be ticked.
Q2: a) 1. When Dave turns the torch on, the light shines from it to the wall.
2. Then he moves the card part way in front of the torch.
3. Part of the light can travel to the wall, but part gets blocked by card.
b) All of the light would get blocked, and none would shine on the wall.

Page 3 Light Travels Into Your Eyes

Q1:

You would be able to see it.	A torch switched on in the dark	A giraffe in the light	Glow worms in the dark	A banana in the light
Gives out light?	Yes	No	Yes	No

You would not be able to see it.	A torch switched off in the dark	A giraffe in the dark	Me in the dark	A banana in the dark
Gives out light?	No	No	No	No

Q2: No — when the torch is switched off it doesn't give out any light, so you can't see it.
Q3: "There is no light" should be circled.
Q4: Because light was shining on them, so you could see them.

Page 4 Light Can Be Reflected

Q1: Around the corner of the wall   Behind the patient's teeth   Behind his shoulder
Q2: When light hits a mirror, the light **IS REFLECTED**. You can see reflections in mirrors, on water, or on **SHINY** surfaces like **WINDOWS**. You can use a mirror to **SEE** what you **LOOK** like, because the light travels from your face to the mirror, where it's **REFLECTED** and comes back to your eyes.

Q3:

Page 5 Light Can Be Reflected

Q1: Traffic Beacon —1   Desk Lamp — 3   Spotlight — 2
Projector — 3   Table lamp — 2

Q2:

Page 6 What Happens when Light is Reflected

Q1: When light hits a mirror, it changes **DIRECTION**. That's why, if you look in a mirror, you can see **YOURSELF**. If the light went straight through the mirror, you'd see **THE BACK OF THE MIRROR**. When you draw a light ray hitting the mirror, you should draw the ray changing direction **WHEN** it hits the mirror.
Q2: When Mr. Grimes shines the torch without the mirror, the light ray goes along line **A**. It lights up the **TENNIS BALL**. After he puts the mirror on the paper, the light goes along line **B**. It lights up the **PLASTIC CARROT**.

Q3:

Page 7 What Happens when Light is Reflected

Q1:

Q2:

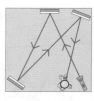

Q3: Set B.

Page 8 Reflecting — Shiny vs Dull

Q1: "Test to see if I can see my face in each one" should be circled.

Q2:

Name of material	Does it reflect?	Is it shiny or dull?
Wood	No	Dull
Silver	Yes	Shiny
Glass	Yes	Shiny
Wool	No	Dull
Rough plastic	No	Dull
Smooth plastic	Yes	Shiny

Q3: The things that reflect are shiny, the ones that don't reflect are dull.
Q4: The metal spoon, the metal saw and the gold bar should be ticked.

Page 9 Shadows

Q1: "Change one distance at a time..." should be circled.
Q2: "If you change two things at once, you wouldn't know which one had made the difference" should be ticked.
Q3: a) Yes   b) No   c) It's a bad idea.

Page 10 Shadows

Q1:

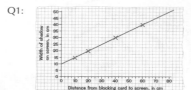

Q2: Yes.
Q3: 25 cm.
Q4: 50 cm.

Page 11 Shadows

Q1:

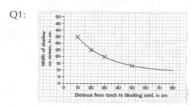

Q2: Yes.
Q3: Anything around 16 cm.
Q4: Anything around 10 cm.

Page 12 Shadows and Reflections

Q1:

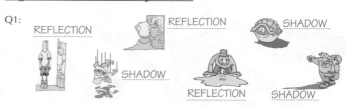

REFLECTION   REFLECTION   SHADOW
SHADOW   REFLECTION   SHADOW

Q2: "Shadows are dark..." and "shadows are made when the light is blocked..." should be ticked. The other three boxes should be crossed.
Q3: Reflections happen when light hits a **SHINY** surface like a mirror, and changes **DIRECTION**. Shadows are made when something is **BLOCKING** the light so there is a **DARK** patch behind it. You can't see details in **SHADOWS**, but you can see details in **REFLECTIONS**.

Revision Questions — How We See Things

At last — bright and shiny revision questions to reflect your knowledge of how we see things.

Q1 a) Circle the things you'd be able to see in a dark room.

| A lit candle | Ace Tomato Sauce | A torch with no batteries in | A brightly coloured pencil case | A searchlight (switched on) | A fire |

b) Why would you be able to see the ones you've picked? Circle the right answer.

I would see them because light would travel from my eyes to the objects.

I would see them because I have x-ray vision.

I would see them because light would travel from the objects to my eyes.

Q2 Fill in the gaps in these sentences using some of the words in the shadow.

When light hits a .... surface, it is reflected.

That's how you see your .... when you look in a

mirror. The light changes .... when it's

reflected, depending on what direction the light has travelled from.

shiny
colour
reflection
light
shadow
dark   dull
direction
surface

Q3 Becki is holding a card in front of a screen and shining a torch onto the card and the screen.

a) She sees a shadow on the screen — why?

....

b) What happens if she moves the card closer to the screen?

....

c) What happens if she moves the torch closer to the card?

....

d) What happens if she turns the torch off?

....

Q4 Draw the light rays travelling from these light sources, by drawing straight lines with arrows on.

Have you seen the light yet?

You should know tons about <u>shadows</u>, <u>reflections</u> and <u>light travelling</u> by now. If you don't, look back over the book to remind yourself. But if you can do these without looking back, that's <u>great</u>.

You Can Change the Brightness of a Bulb

You might think that once you've got your bulb connected in a circuit, you can't change how bright it is. Wrong — you can change the brightness of any bulb by fiddling with the circuit. Watch and grin...

Q1 Have a bash at this. You've got to fill in the blanks, using some of the words on the right.

You can make this bulb brighter by adding another

.... to the circuit. Or you could

use a battery with a .... But if you

added another .... to the circuit,

there would be less .... for each

bulb, so both bulbs would be ....

than the original one.

Words: brighter, water, battery, food, bulb, power, bigger engine, lower voltage, dimmer, higher voltage

Q2 For each of these pairs of circuits, tick the one where the bulb (or bulbs) will be brighter. Then say why.

a)

Why? ....

b)

Why? ....

c)

Why? ....

Ellie decided to make her bulbs brighter by painting them.

d)

Why? ....

I wish I could make myself a bit brighter...

The power comes from the battery. To get **more power**, add **another battery** or use a stronger one. If you add **more bulbs**, they have to **share** the power between them, so each bulb will be **dimmer**.

You Can Change the Speed of a Motor

Changing the speed of a motor is pretty much like changing the brightness of a bulb — when you put <u>more battery power</u> through a motor, you make it <u>work faster</u>. And you get more battery power by adding <u>more batteries</u>, or by using a <u>higher voltage</u> battery.

Q1   Look at these circuits and work out which motor will run faster out of each pair. Write FASTER or SLOWER under each one.

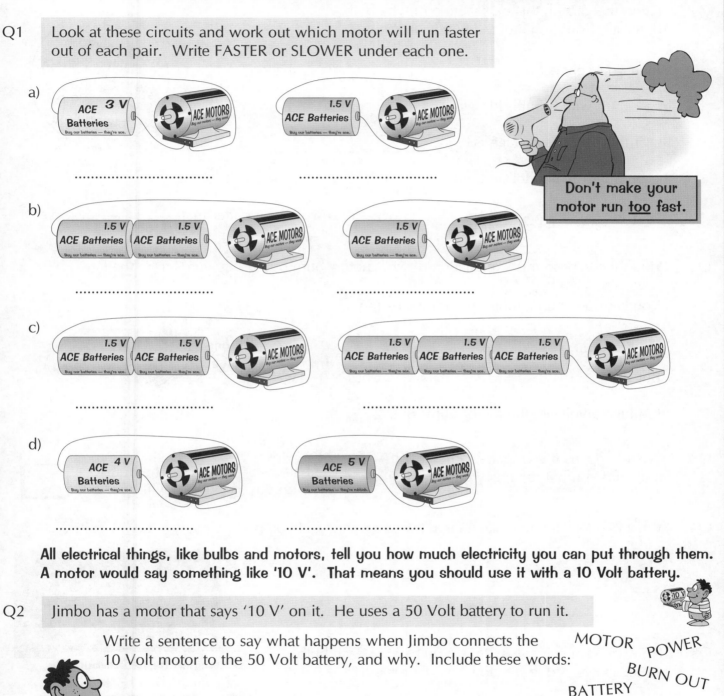

a)

....

Don't make your motor run <u>too</u> fast.

b)

....

c)

....

d)

....

All electrical things, like bulbs and motors, tell you how much electricity you can put through them. A motor would say something like '10 V'. That means you should use it with a 10 Volt battery.

Q2   Jimbo has a motor that says '10 V' on it. He uses a 50 Volt battery to run it.

Write a sentence to say what happens when Jimbo connects the 10 Volt motor to the 50 Volt battery, and why. Include these words:

MOTOR   POWER   BURN OUT   BATTERY

....

....

....

Speed up your motor — put it on the fast train to London...

You can <u>change</u> the speed of a motor, or the brightness of a bulb, by changing the <u>battery power</u> for them. But <u>beware</u> — if you put too much power through them, they <u>just can't handle it</u>.

Too Much Power Will Burn Things Out

You can make bulbs brighter and motors faster by giving them <u>more power</u>. But if you try putting 20 Volts through a tiny little 2 Volt bulb, it's just gonna give up on you and go '<u>ping</u>', and that'll be it.

Q1 Fill in the gaps in this explanation of why bulbs burn out, using some of the words on the bulb.

(words on bulb: brighter, more powerful, too high, burn out, gas, dimmer, can't, too low, glow brightly, can*)*

When you connect a .... battery

in a circuit with a bulb, it'll glow ....

But if the battery's voltage is ....,

the bulb gets really hot and will ....

And you .... get it to work again after that.

Q2 Fill in the gaps in this explanation of why motors burn out, using words from the fan.

You can speed up a motor by using a battery

with a ....

But if the .... has

too high a voltage, the motor burns out.

(words on fan: motor, nice hat, higher voltage, battery*)*

ACE MOTORS

Q3 What happens if you make a circuit with a bulb and you put too many batteries in it?

Tick the right answer.

The battery will burn out. ☐   The bulb will burn out. ☐

Q4 What happens if you make a circuit with a motor and you put too many batteries in it?

....

....

Bill wished he hadn't burnt out the bulb in his torch.

Q5 Here are some circuits with 3 V bulbs. For each bulb, write "glows", "doesn't glow" or "burns out".

ACE 3 V Batteries — ACE 3 V Batteries   ACE 3 V Batteries   ACE 9 V Batteries

....

Aaargghh, too much power — I think I'm gonna explode...

Bang.

Circuit Diagrams and Symbols

Drawing a good diagram of a circuit means that <u>anyone</u> could build it, by using your plan.

Q1   Fill in the gaps in these sentences about road signs
using some of the words from the sign on the right.

Road signs .... have lots of writing on them.

For example, a 'no ....' sign

like this doesn't have any writing on it — just

a crossed out picture of a left arrow. That's

useful because it's .... and easy to ....

SLOW
DON'T DO
LEFT TURN QUICK
UNDERSTAND RIGHT TURN

Q2   Prof. Bighair, Mr. Batry and Sir Kit share an assistant. They've given her drawings of circuits they need — here are the pictures they drew and photos of the circuits they actually wanted.

nee naw

ACE BATTERIES

ACE MOTORS 6V

3V ACE BUZZER

a)   Why might the assistant have problems building the circuits? Tick the right answers.

The same part looks
different in each drawing. ☐

There are no batteries
in any of the circuits. ☐

The circuits are
impossible to build. ☐

She might not be able to tell the difference
between motors and batteries in the drawings. ☐

b)   Circle the best way to get around these problems.

Only let one person
in the world draw
circuit diagrams.

Have a set of symbols so that
everyone draws the parts of
circuits in the same way.

Only let assistants
work for one
scientist at a time.

Are you all right? — Yes, I'm a 'no left turn' sign...

It makes sense for everyone to use the <u>same symbols</u> to draw circuit diagrams. If everyone drew things their own way then diagrams would look like the ones on this page — pretty useless.

Circuit Diagrams and Symbols

It's a good idea for everyone to use the <u>same</u> symbols — now <u>you</u>'ve got to <u>learn</u> them.

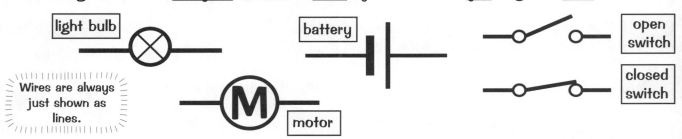

Wires are always just shown as lines.

Q1 Alison's trying to make some circuits. Write under each one whether she's got it RIGHT or WRONG.

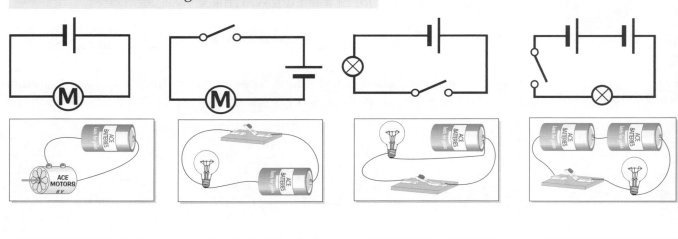

....

Q2 Match up the diagrams of circuits to the right picture by drawing a line between them.

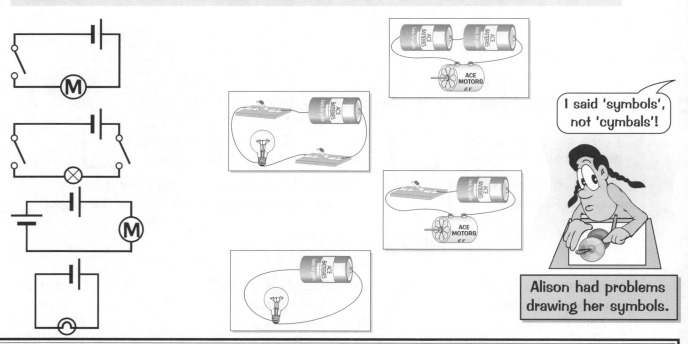

I said 'symbols', not 'cymbals'!

Alison had problems drawing her symbols.

It'd be noisy if everyone used the same cymbals...

Hopefully by now you're pretty hot at comparing <u>normal pictures</u> to <u>circuit diagrams</u>. And don't worry if it all seems a bit fiddly — there are tons more to play around with on the next page...

Circuit Diagrams and Symbols

I suppose you thought you'd get away without drawing any diagrams <u>yourself</u>. Well, think again.

Q1 Draw circuit diagrams for these circuits in the boxes.

Q2 You knew it was coming — now draw realistic pictures for each of these circuit diagrams.

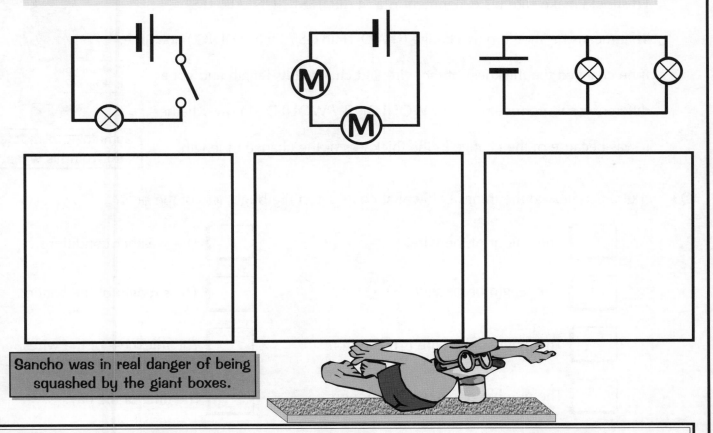

Sancho was in real danger of being squashed by the giant boxes.

Pancake Olympics — with batter-y circuits...

I don't know about you, but I'm completely sick of drawing circuits now. At least you can consider yourself a real <u>pro</u> at turning pictures into <u>proper diagrams</u> — now you can sleep easy at night.

Wire Thickness — Fair Tests

'HCC', the Huge Computer Company, want to build a computer with a brand new feature on it called the "You've-left-the-computer-on-again-der-brain light" (or "YLTCOADB light" for short). It's made up of <u>long wires</u> that go from the computer to the front door where there's a <u>little bulb</u> that lights up really <u>brightly</u> to tell you that the computer's still on.

Q1 Read the computer screen and then put a (circle) around the way Ed should do the experiment.

> ED DENING, THE HEAD BOFFIN AT HCC HAS BEEN GIVEN THE JOB OF INVESTIGATING WHICH WIRES TO USE. HE THINKS THIN WIRES WILL MAKE THE BULB DIMMER, BUT HE NEEDS TO DO AN EXPERIMENT TO BE SURE.

Test wires of different lengths.

Test lots of wire of the same thickness.

Guess.

Test several thicknesses of wires and see how bright the bulb is.

Test the same wires with different numbers of bulbs.

Test the stretchiness of the wire.

Test wires of different colours.

Q2 Cross out the wrong words from the brackets to make this paragraph right.

Ed should make sure his experiment is a (FAIR TEST / UNFAIR TEST).

That means he should only change (TWO THINGS / ONE THING) at a time.

If he changed the thickness of the wire <u>and</u> changed its length and got a

different result from before, he (WOULDN'T / WOULD) know whether

it was because of the change in the thickness or the change in length.

What are you looking at?

Something distracted Ed from his wires.

Q3 Put a tick next to the things below that could affect the brightness of the bulb.

☐ The colour of the wire.	☐ The weather conditions.
☐ The length of the wire.	☐ The strength of the battery.
☐ The material the wire is made from.	☐ The thickness of the wires.
☐ The number of people in the room.	☐ The time of the day.

Supernatural-flying-elf exam — a fairy test...

I doubt if the words '<u>fair test</u>' are new to you because we've been banging on more than burning sausages in a firework factory. That's because it's very, **VERY** important.

Wire Thickness — Results

Now it's the time you've been waiting for — yep, it's <u>experiment</u> time.

Q1 Tick the box next to the circuit you should use to do Ed's experiment.

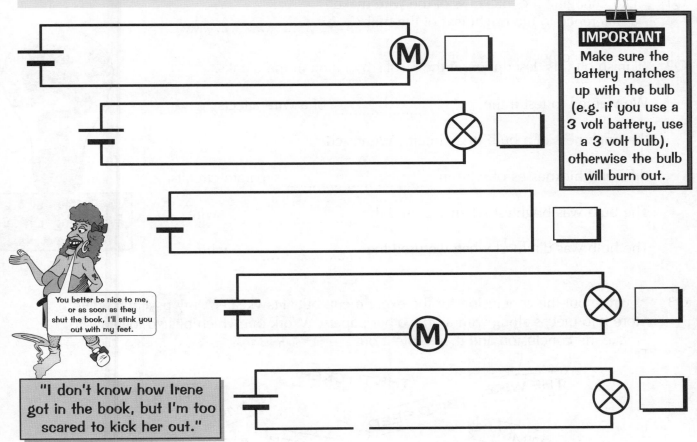

IMPORTANT
Make sure the battery matches up with the bulb (e.g. if you use a 3 volt battery, use a 3 volt bulb), otherwise the bulb will burn out.

"You better be nice to me, or as soon as they shut the book, I'll stink you out with my feet."

"I don't know how Irene got in the book, but I'm too scared to kick her out."

Q2 Follow the instructions below to do the experiment and complete the table.
(If you can't do the experiment there are spare results at the bottom of the page for you to use.)

1) Make three circuits with 3 different thicknesses of wire. One with thin wire (use 0.1 mm fuse wire), one with thick wire (use 0.5 mm fuse wire) and with very thick wire (use 1 mm fuse wire).

Each circuit should use two 1 metre long wires and should be set up like the correct answer to Q1.

2) When all three circuits are connected up, look at the three bulbs and compare the brightness.

3) In the 'thickness of wire' side of the table write down 'thin', 'thick' and 'very thick'.

4) Write in the 'brightness of bulb' side 'brightest', 'next brightest' and 'dimmest'.

Thickness of wire	Brightness of bulb

Spare Results: very thick wire = brightest; thick wire = next brightest; thin wire = dimmest.

"Wire we here?" — "Ask the bulb, she's bright"...

Connect the circuit up right, <u>match</u> the bulb to the battery and make sure the wires are all the <u>same length</u> — once you've taken care of all that, things should run smoother than a bobsled.

MINI-PROJECT

Wire Thicknesses — Conclusions

You've done the experiment, now you need to write
down what you found out, in proper <u>scientific</u> speak.

Q1 Did changing the thickness of the wire make
a difference to the brightness of the bulb? ....

Q2 Finish off this description of the results by filling in the blanks.

We wanted to test if the .... of a wire affects

the brightness of a bulb in a circuit. We tested ....

different thicknesses of wire in .... separate circuits.

The bulb was brightest when we used the .... wire.

The bulb was dimmest when we used the .... wire.

New Genie bulbs give
everlasting light and
two free wishes.

Q3 I wrote out the conclusion for the experiment, but "Hawkeater", my psycho-budgie,
tore it to pieces along with all my other papers. Work out which bits go together to
make the conclusion and then write it out. (Hint: You need 10 bits of paper, including full stops.)

THE WIRE   THE THICKER   THE WIRE   THE BULB

BIRD SEED   THE DIMMER   THE BRIGHTER   THE THINNER

ROMEO, ROMEO   THE BULB

....

....

Q4 Which wire should Ed use to make the YLTCOADB light? ....

Q5 The button part of my doorbell is connected, with long wires, to the bell bit that's upstairs.
At the moment it rings too loudly. What can I do to make it quieter? (Tick the right answer.)

Replace the wires with thicker ones. ☐   **Replace the wires with thinner ones.** ☐

I put the bulb in backwards — I started to blub...

Don't go thinking the conclusion part of the experiment is just an unimportant bit of waffle at the
end, because it <u>ain't</u>. Conclusions make sense of results in a <u>simple</u>, <u>easy-to-read</u> way. So there.

Testing Different Wires

MINI-PROJECT

The thickness of wire isn't the <u>only</u> thing that changes how bright a bulb shines or how loud a bell rings — what the wire's <u>made of</u> will also have an effect.

Q1   Ed is going to make wires out of different materials. Then he's going to test each wire to see which one makes the bulb shine the brightest. There's no point testing ones that don't conduct electricity so put a cross through each material below that doesn't.

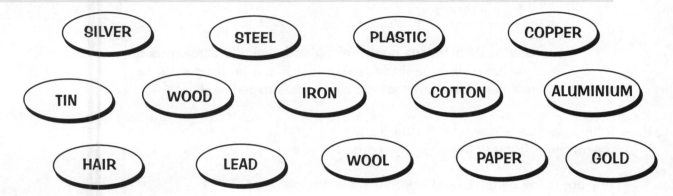

SILVER   STEEL   PLASTIC   COPPER

TIN   WOOD   IRON   COTTON   ALUMINIUM

HAIR   LEAD   WOOL   PAPER   GOLD

Q2   Ed carried out the experiment with 4 materials and wrote his results in a pad. Write the results in the table in order of brightness (brightest last).

Type of wire	Brightness of bulb

Wire exp. results:

I tested 4 different types of wire: Lead, Gold, Copper and Iron. I gave each a score out of 10 for how bright the bulb shone. 10 = the brightest. The Lead wires scored 4, the Gold wires scored 10, the Copper wires scored 8 and the Iron wires scored 7.

Q3   Which type of wire should Ed use?   ....

Q4   How would you test whether different lengths of wire affect the brightness of the bulb?

....

....

Wires made of trees — that wood knot work...

<u>No matter what</u> you're testing, you've got to make sure it's the <u>only thing</u> you change in the experiment. Unless it's a very long experiment, in which case you can change your clothes as well.

Using Your Knowledge of Circuits

Abe and Belinda are doing some experiments with circuits. Here's a picture of one of their circuits:

Battery

Bare wire

Bulb

One of their friends comes along and says it's dangerous to use bare wires. Belinda replies that it can be dangerous to use bare wire, but that it's safe in this experiment.

Q1 Belinda forgets to say <u>why</u> it isn't dangerous for their experiment. Put a tick next to the correct reason.

They are using batteries and not mains electricity, so the voltage is low enough not to be dangerous.

The batteries they are using are flat, so there is no electrical current at all.

They are being very careful not to touch the bare wire.

Abe thought he needed to catch a wiry bear for the experiments.

Q2 Fill in the gaps in this sentence using the words in the box. There are more words than you need.

It's .... to use bare wire with batteries, because the voltage is so ....

that it isn't dangerous. Bare wires connected to the .... are very ....

You should .... have bare wires on a mains electricity circuit.

HIGH   LOW   MAINS   OK   ILLEGAL   DANGEROUS   SOMETIMES   KETTLE   NEVER

Q3 Here's a list of materials. (Ring) the ones that would make good insulators for mains wire.

Rubber   Wax   Chocolate   Copper
      Tin foil   Cotton   Plastic

Q4 Why would the ones you've ringed make good insulators? (There are two reasons.)

....

Bare wires — I hope they're not too embarrassed...

Easy enough really — bare wire is <u>dangerous</u> if it has a fairly high voltage travelling through it, but you can make it safe by covering it with a good flexible <u>insulator</u>, like plastic. Nice.

Revision Questions — Changing Circuits

I've packed this page full to bursting with jolly questions,
but it's not just there to look pretty — you'd better get on with it.

Q1 a) What could you add to this circuit to make the bulb <u>brighter</u>?

....

b) What could you add to the circuit to make the bulb <u>dimmer</u>? Why would this work?

....

Q2 Would one of these motors turn faster than the other? Explain why or why not.

....

....

Q3 Tick the circuit diagram Tim's drawn correctly and put a cross next to the one he's got wrong.

Q4 Draw a circuit diagram for this circuit.

Q5 Tick the bulb that'll shine the brightest.

(both wires are the same length)

thick wire   thin wire

Q6 I want to make the bulb in this circuit shine as brightly as I can — should I make the wires out of copper, gold or plastic? Why are the other two materials not as good?

....

....

"Don't look," said the circuit — "I'm changing"...

Now's the time to go back through the book and read up on anything you thought was a bit <u>chewy</u>. And that, my friend, is <u>that</u>. No more circuits, no more torches or mirrors, just a nice, juicy index.

Index